W9-APO-265

Our Family
by Linda Spivey

ISBN 1-57977-132-7

Published by Havoc Publishing
San Diego, California

Please write to us for more information
on Havoc Publishing products.

Havoc Publishing
6330 Nancy Ridge Drive, Suite 104
San Diego, California 92121

Made in China

A Family is Forever - A Circle of Strength & Love
A statement about our family:
A Family Stays Together and Warms the Heart

CONTENTS

CONTENTS

Anyone can count the seeds in an apple ~ Only God can count the apples in a seed.
Our Family Tree
L.Spivey ©

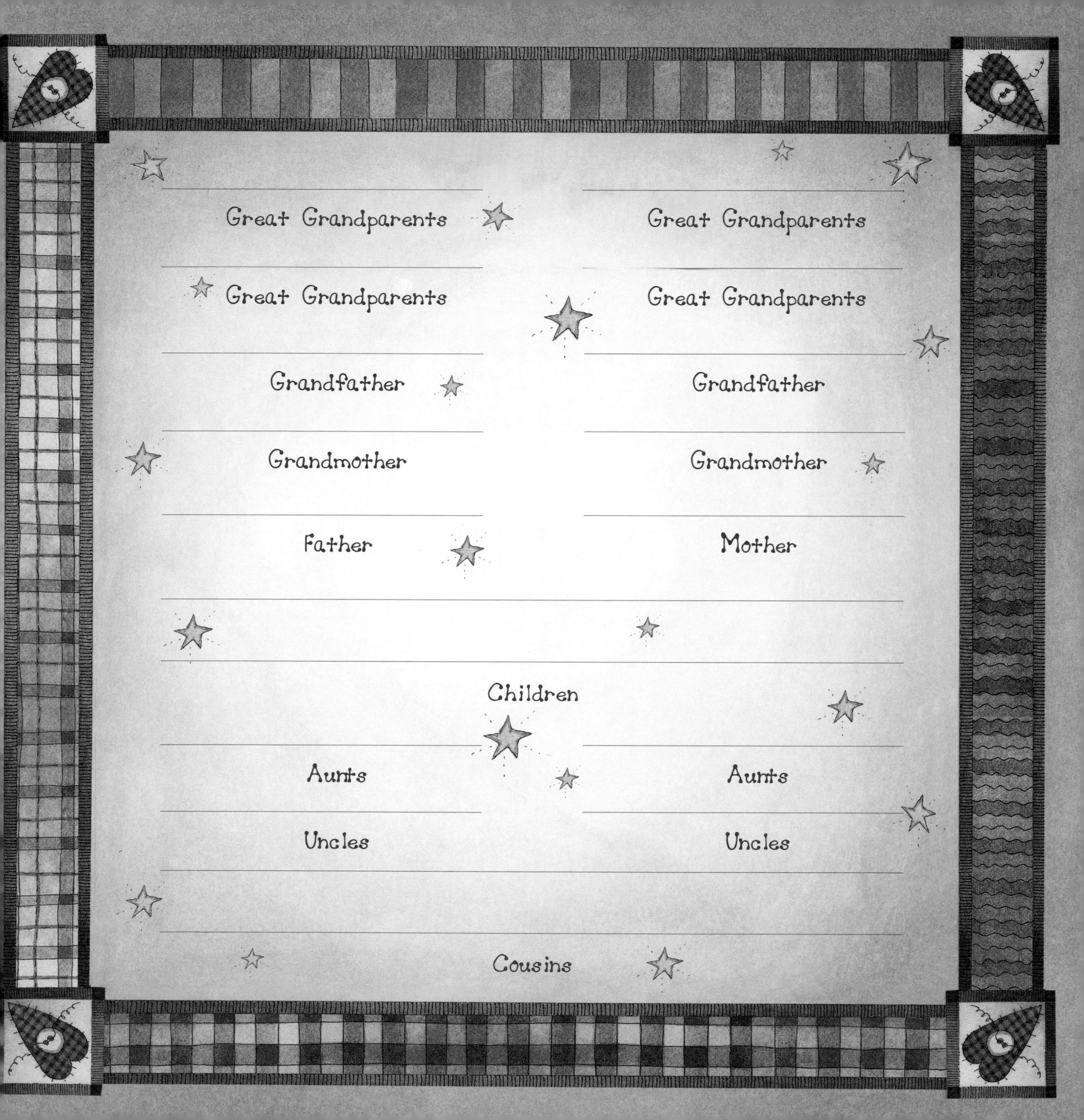

Great Grandparents
Great Grandparents
Great Grandparents
Great Grandparents
Grandfather
Grandfather
Grandmother
Grandmother
Father
Mother
Children
Aunts
Aunts
Uncles
Uncles
Cousins

These are our Great Grandparents

(Father's Father's Family)

Great Grandfather's full name ______________________

Date & place he was born ______________________

When growing up he lived ______________________

Jobs he held ______________________

Interests and hobbies ______________________

Our favorite story about him ______________________

____

Great Grandmother's full name ______________________

Date & place she was born ______________________

When growing up she lived ______________________

Jobs she held ______________________

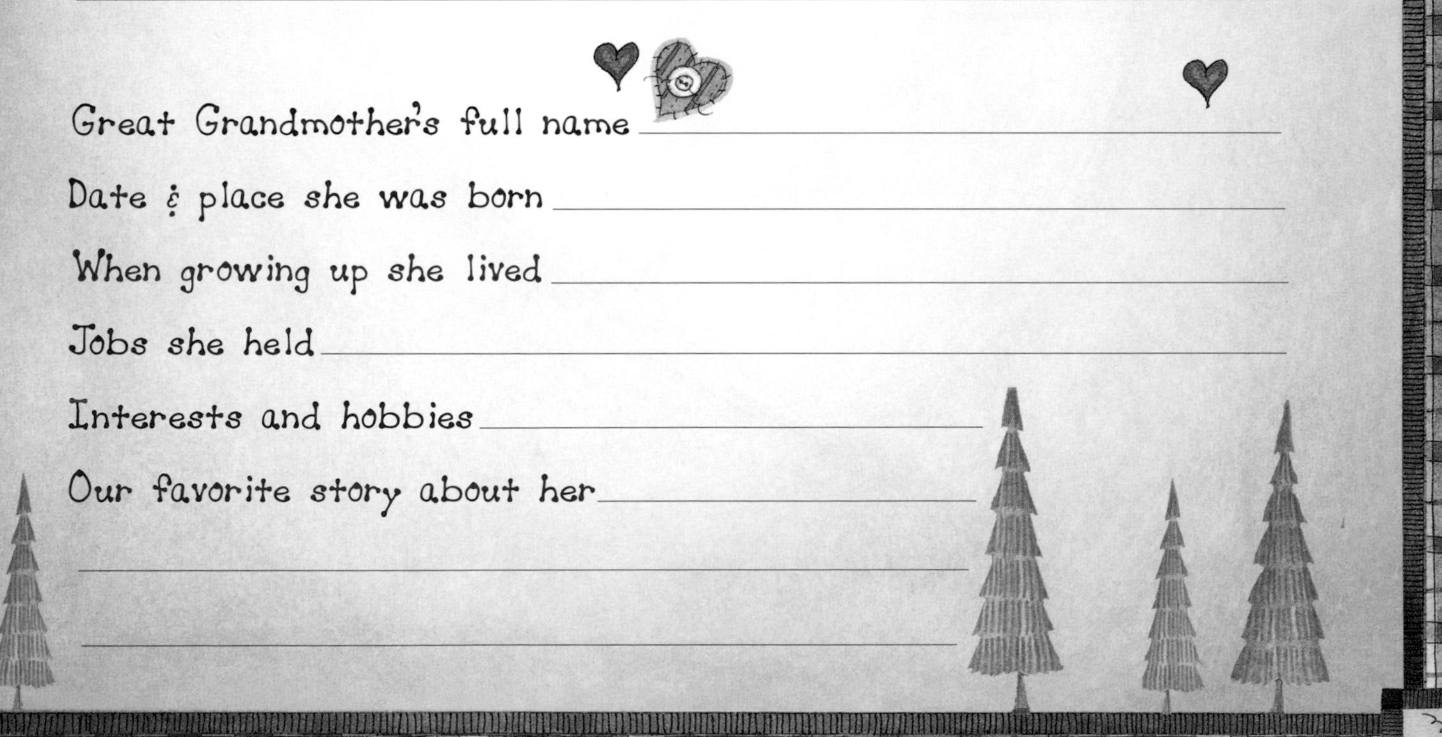

Interests and hobbies ______________________

Our favorite story about her ______________________

____

____

These are our Great Grandparents

(Father's Mother's Family)

Great Grandfather's full name ______________________________

Date & place he was born ______________________________

When growing up he lived ______________________________

Jobs he held ______________________________

Interests and hobbies ______________________________

Our favorite story about him ______________________________

____

Great Grandmother's full name ______________________________

Date & place she was born ______________________________

When growing up she lived ______________________________

Jobs she held ______________________________

Interests and hobbies ______________________________

Our favorite story about her ______________________________

____

____

These are our Grandparents

(Father's Family)

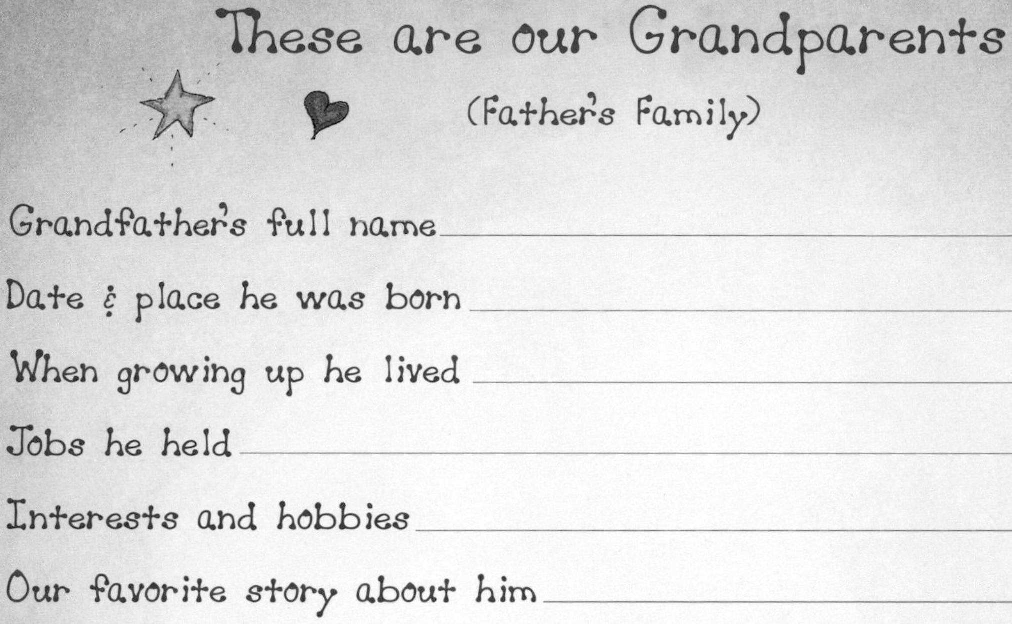

Grandfather's full name ______________________

Date & place he was born ______________________

When growing up he lived ______________________

Jobs he held ______________________

Interests and hobbies ______________________

Our favorite story about him ______________________

____

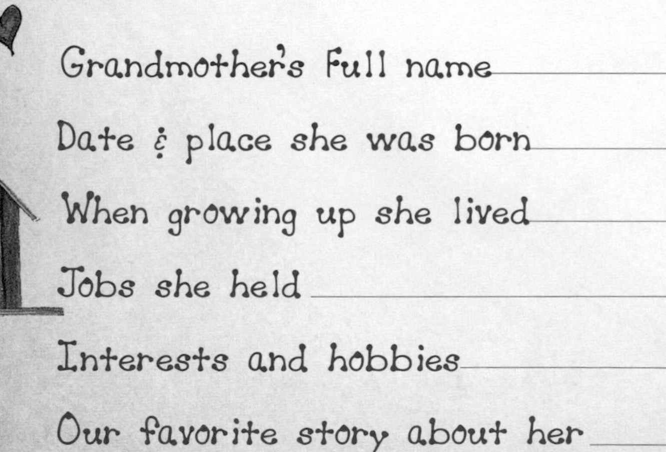

Grandmother's Full name ______________________

Date & place she was born ______________________

When growing up she lived ______________________

Jobs she held ______________________

Interests and hobbies ______________________

Our favorite story about her ______________________

____

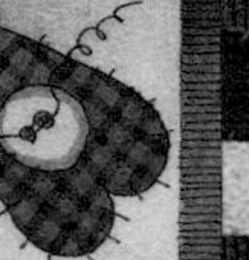

How Grandpa and Grandma met

(Father's Family)

How they met ______________________________

____

____

____

The ages of both ______________________________

The date they were married ______________________________

The address of their first home was ______________________________

____

The names of their children are ______________________________

____

____

This is our Father

Father's full name *Jason Aaron Smith*

Date he was born *August 26, 1974*

Place he was born *Centralia, Illinois*

When growing up he lived

Jobs he held

Interests and hobbies

Our favorite story about him

Photo

Aunts, Uncles, and Cousins

(Father's Family)

Names *Aunt Susan . Uncle Mike* ____________________

Where they live *Tennessee* ____________________

When we get together to visit ____________________

Activities we do with them ____________________

These are our Great Grandparents

(Mother's Father's Family)

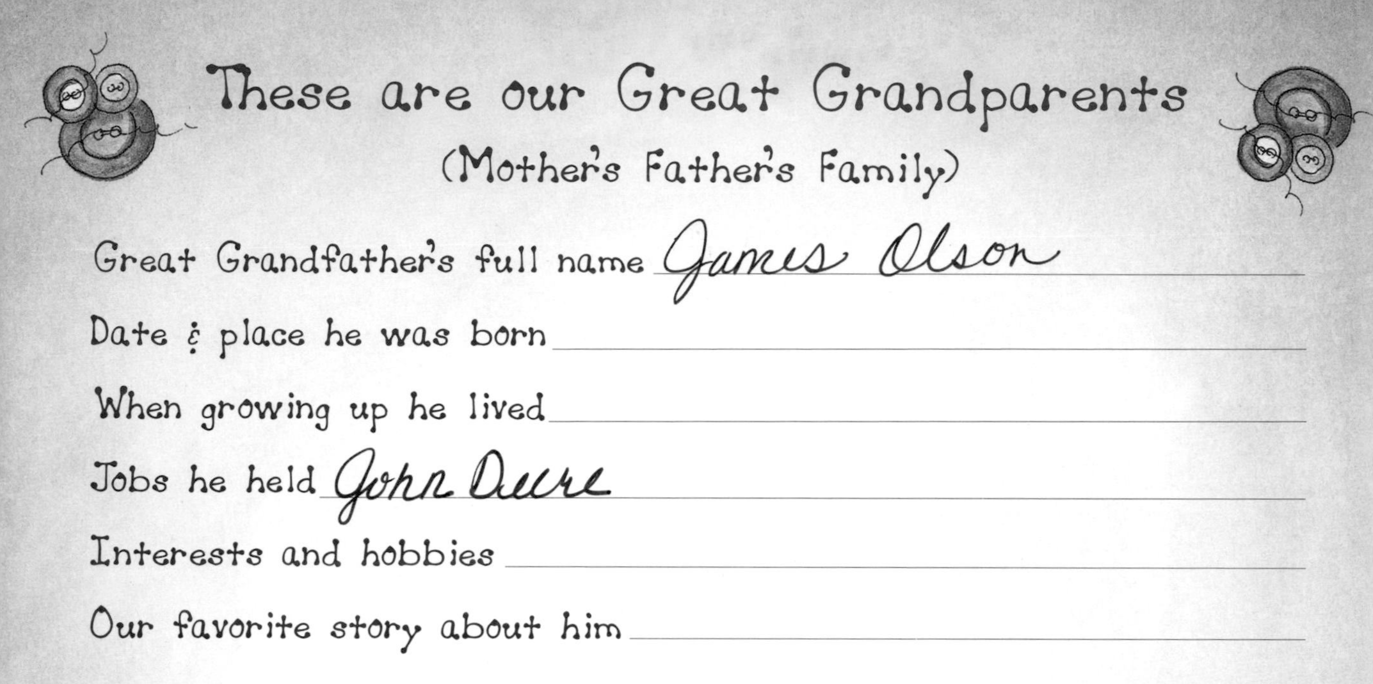

Great Grandfather's full name James Olson

Date & place he was born

When growing up he lived

Jobs he held John Deere

Interests and hobbies

Our favorite story about him

Great Grandmother's full name Dell Olson

Date & place she was born

When growing up she lived

Jobs she held

Interests and hobbies

Our favorite story about her

These are our Great Grandparents

(Mother's Mother's Family)

Great Grandfather's full name James Barlett

Date & place he was born

When growing up he lived

Jobs he held

Interests and hobbies

Our favorite story about him

Great Grandmother's full name [illegible] Jean Barlett

Date & place she was born

When growing up she lived

Jobs she held

Interests and hobbies

Our favorite story about her

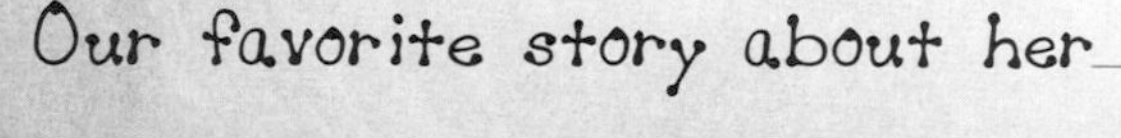

These are our Grandparents

(Mother's Family)

Grandfather's full name Tim Olson

Date & place he was born ______

When growing up he lived East Moline, Illinois

Jobs he held ______

Interests and hobbies ______

Our favorite story about him ______

______

Grandmother's Full name Debbie Olson

Date & place she was born ______

When growing up she lived Orion, Illinois

Jobs she held ______

Interests and hobbies ______

Our favorite story about her ______

______

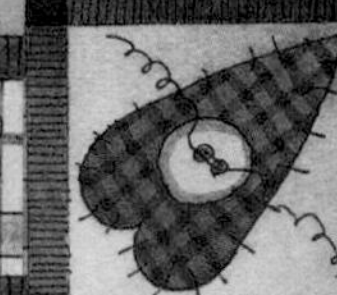

How Grandpa and Grandma met

(Mother's Family)

How they met ______

The ages of both ______

The date they were married ______

The address of their first home was ______

The names of their children are ______

This is our Mother

Mother's full name Krustyna Marie Smith

Date she was born January 19, 1977

Place she was born Moline, Illinois

When growing up she lived East Moline, Illinois

Jobs she held State Farm

Interests and hobbies

Our favorite story about her

Photograph

Aunts, Uncles, and Cousins

(Mother's Family)

Names Aunt Ashley

Uncle Tim

Where they live

Uncle Tim lives in NY

When we get together to visit

Activities we do with them

Photograph

Photograph

United in Marriage
Date
October 30, 1999
Kristyna Marie
&
Jason Aaron
(names)

How our Mother and Father met

How they met ______________________

The ages of both ______________________

The date they were married *October 30, 1999*

The ceremony *Church of Christ, United*
Lexington, Illinois

Special people that attended ______________________

These are the Children in our Family

Names & birth dates

James Cole, May 29, 2005

Jason McHarry "Mac", September 7, 2007

Distinct personalities

Jimmy - Shy

Mac - Loud

Aa·Bb·Cc·Dd·Ee·Ff·Gg·Hh·Ii·Jj·Kk·Ll·Mm·Nn·Oo·Pp·Qq·Rr·Ss·Tt·Uu·Vv·Ww·Xx·Yy·Zz·1·2·3
Signatures of children
RED
GREEN
MOMMY

Friends are Family too!

Names of our special family friends Candy, Chris, Dennise

Craig, Mike, Bob

They are special to us because

How long we have known them years!

Our favorite things to do together

Cookout

Friends
are
family
too!

HAPPY
BIRTHDA
HAPPY BIRTH
HAPPY BIRTHDAY

Birthdays

List birthdays

How we celebrate

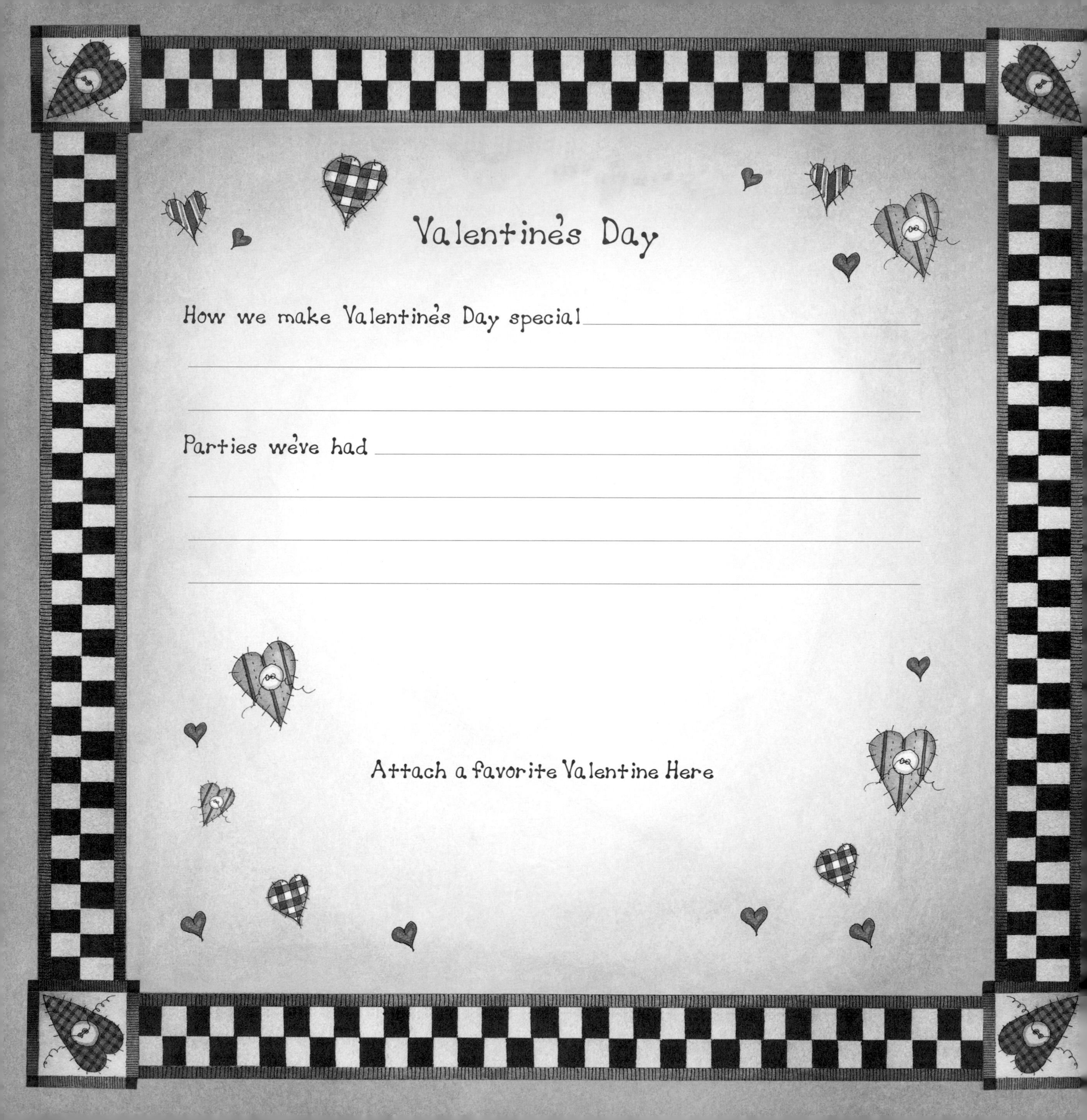

Valentine's Day

How we make Valentine's Day special ______________________

____

____

Parties we've had ______________________

____

____

____

Attach a favorite Valentine Here

Photographs

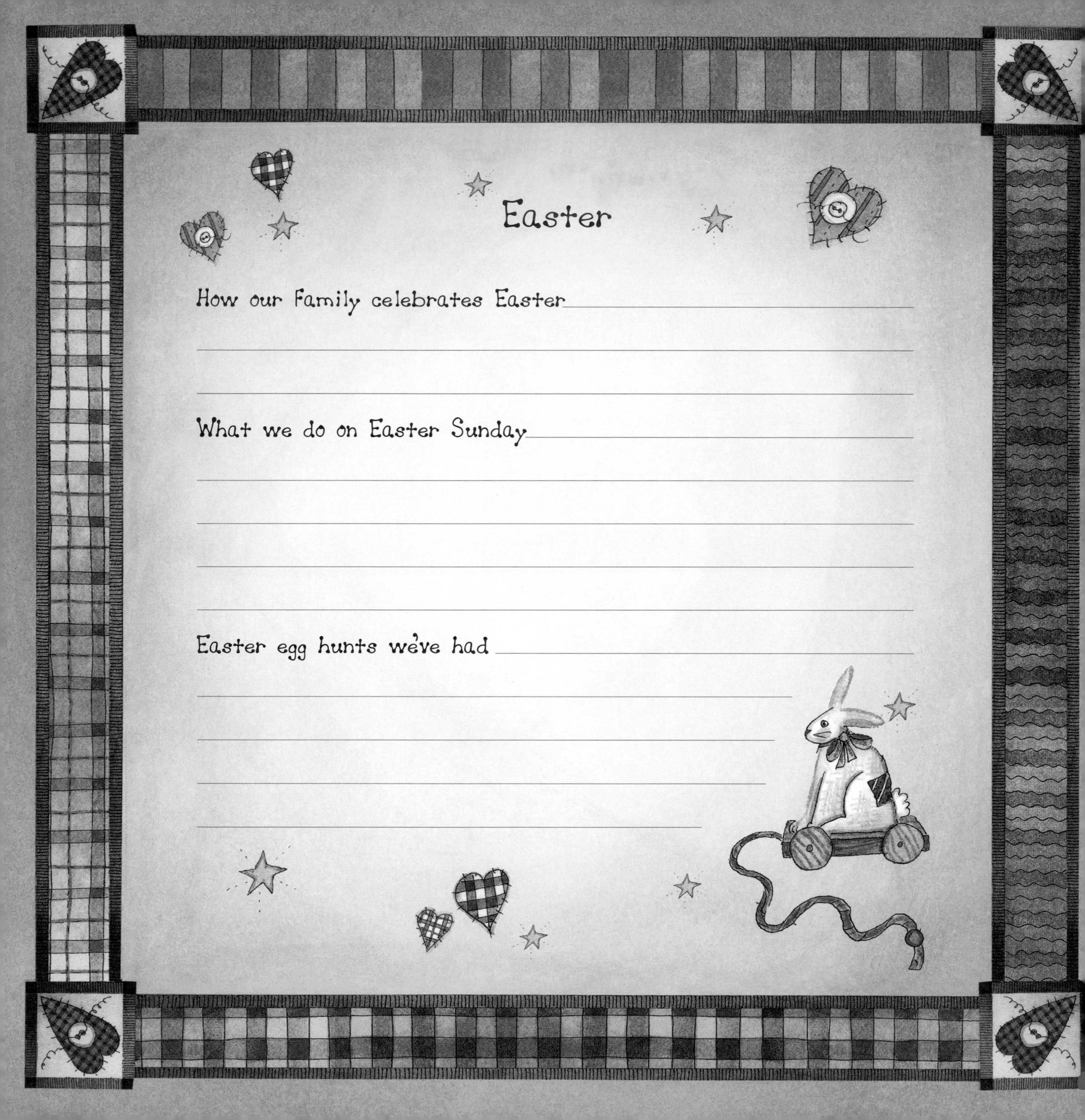

Easter

How our Family celebrates Easter

What we do on Easter Sunday

Easter egg hunts we've had

Happy Easter

Halloween

Our best, funniest, and scariest costumes worn ____________________

____

____

Our favorite Trick-or-Treat story ____________________

____

Favorite party we had ____________________

____

____

____

Photographs

Thanksgiving

Where we celebrate Thanksgiving

Thanksgiving traditions

Who prepares our meal

What we feast on

Turkey stories

Christmas

How and when we decorate for Christmas

How we spend Christmas Eve

Where we spend Christmas

There's no place like home for the Holidays
L Spivey©

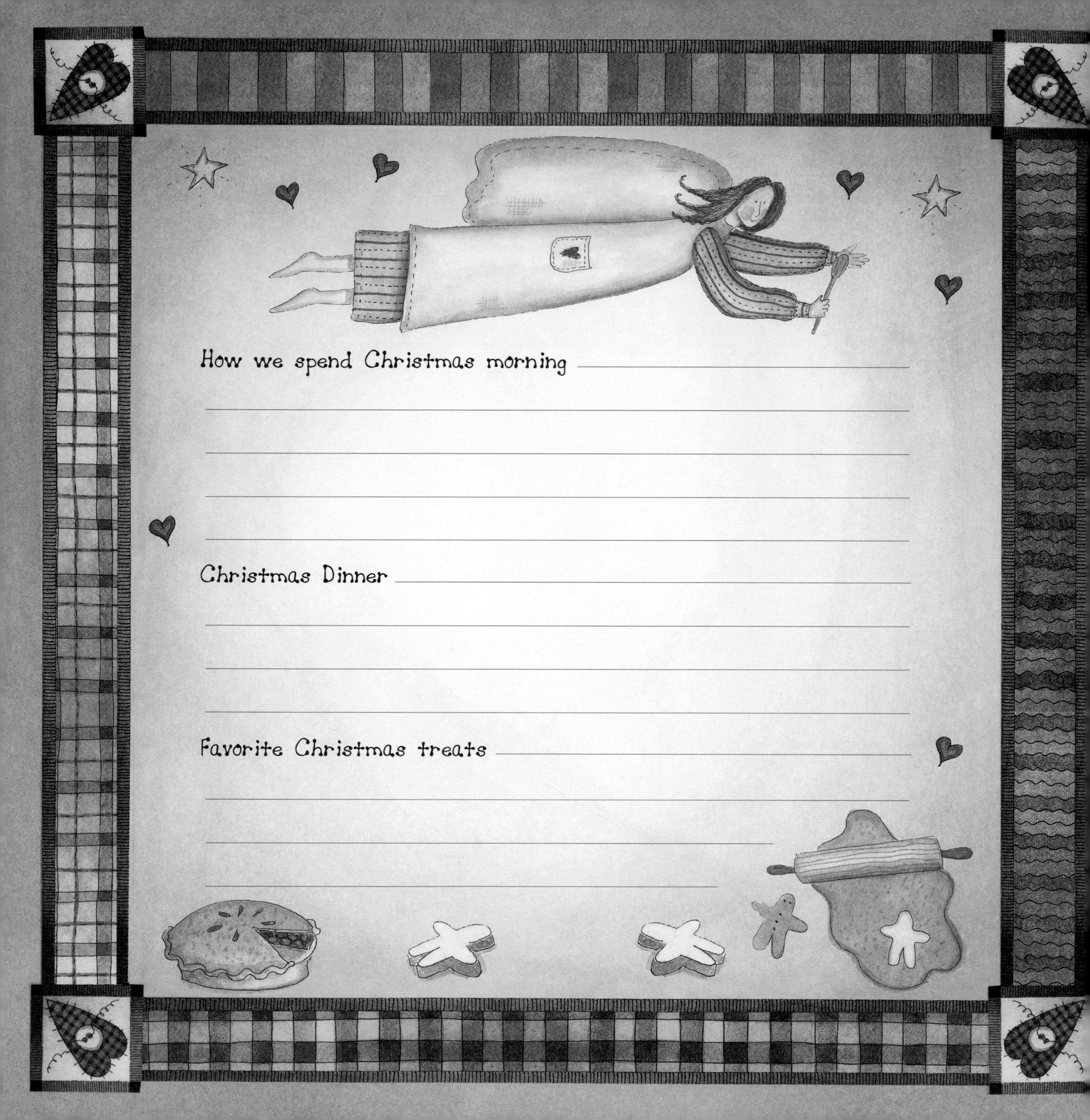

How we spend Christmas morning

Christmas Dinner

Favorite Christmas treats

Photographs

Traditions

Family traditions

Places we go

Every year we

Special days spent with our family

Traditions create a bond which envelopes
us in security and warmth

Caring
Happiness is made to be Shared
Love Doubles Our Joy and Divides Sorrow
Warm Hearts
Memories
ugs and Kisses
Sharing
Laughing

Family Homes

A House Becomes a Home if it Holds All of Us

Where our family has lived ______________________

How long we have lived there ______________________

Addresses ______________________

What our house is/was like ______________________

Favorite neighbors and funny stories ______________________

God Bless this Home

Our Family Heritage

History is a Circle Never Ending, but Always Going Round

What ethnic groups make up our family ____________________

____

How our family came to this country ____________________

____

____

____

Special foods, sayings, and customs we have in our family ____________________

____

____

____

____

____

____

Religion

Our family's religious background ______________________

____

We attend this place of worship ______________________

____

Our Ministers' names are ______________________

____

____

Our friends who attend with us ______________________

____

____

What we do after service ______________________

____

____

____

Photograph

Photograph

Sports

Sports our family enjoys ____________________

____

Who is involved in which sport ____________________

____

Championships, trophies and awards ____________________

____

Famous sports stories ____________________

____

____

____

Photograph

GO TEA
LSpivey©

Music Makes Our Hearts Sing

Songs our family sings ______________________

____

Lullabies we grew up with ______________________

____

Songs we sing at holiday time ______________________

____

____

Family member and instrument played ______________________

____

Family Activities

Movies we like to watch ______________________________

____

Books we've all read and enjoyed ______________________________

____

Arts and crafts we do together ______________________________

____

Board/card games we play ______________________________

____

Other activities ______________________________

____

Photograph

Photograph

Let's Eat

Favorite family foods ____________________

Favorite restaurants ____________________

Likes and dislikes ____________________

Family Favorite Recipes
Jam
Flour
Flour
Flour
SUGAR
XXXX

Family Chores

Family chores ______________________________

____

Who does them ______________________________

____

Our favorite story about family chores ______________________________

____

____

Chore
List

Animals are Family too!

Family pets ______________________________

How they came to be a part of our family ______________________________

____

How they got their names ______________________________

____

Pet tricks, personalities and stories ______________________________

All creatures great and small, the Lord God made them all........

Have Each Family Member Record
a Special Memory:

Have Each Family Member Record
a Special Memory:

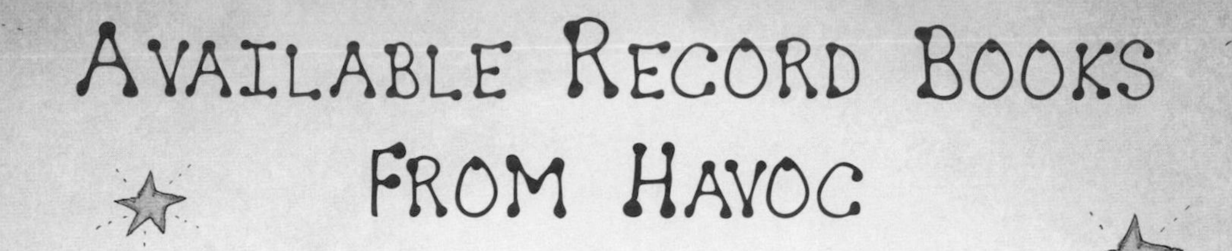

Baby
Coach
College Life
Couples
Dad
Family
Forever Friends
Girlfriends
Golf
Grandmother
Grandparents

Mom
Mothers & Daughters
My Pregnancy
Our Honeymoon
Retirement
School Days
Single Life
Sisters
Teacher
Traveling Adventures
Tying the Knot

havoc™ PUBLISHING

Please write to us with your ideas for
additional Havoc Publishing products

Havoc Publishing
6330 Nancy Ridge Drive, Suite 104
San Diego, CA 92121